A play by
Steve Barlow and
Steve Skidmore

A QUIET FAMILY
CHRISTMAS

Illustrations by
Lesley Danson

THE FAMILY OF KING HENRY VIII

First Wife
CATHERINE OF ARAGON
(married 1509, divorced 1533)
Daughter – **MARY**

Second Wife
ANNE BOLEYN
(married 1533, beheaded 1536)
Daughter – **ELIZABETH**

Third Wife
JANE SEYMOUR
(married 1536, died 1537)
Son – **EDWARD**

Fourth Wife
ANNE OF CLEVES
(married 1540, divorced 1540)

Fifth Wife
CATHERINE HOWARD
(married 1540, beheaded 1542)

By December of 1542, Henry wanted to marry again.

Mary
King Henry's daughter, aged 26. Henry divorced her mother so he could marry Anne Boleyn. Very religious.

Elizabeth
Henry's daughter, aged nine. Her mother, Anne Boleyn, was beheaded. Cheerful and chatty, but stubborn.

Edward
Henry's son, aged five. His mother died when he was born. He is spoilt.

Will Sommers
King Henry's jester.

Catherine Parr
Catherine is 31. She looks after Mary and Elizabeth. She is kind and sensible.

Thomas Seymour
A lord who wants to marry Catherine Parr.

3

Hampton Court Palace, Christmas Eve, 1542.

A candlelit room. Catherine Parr and Thomas Seymour enter. Thomas is carrying some Christmas presents.

Thomas Catherine, when are we going to get married?

Catherine Look out, Thomas, you're dropping the presents.

Thomas drops some of the presents. Catherine picks them up and puts them back in his arms.

Thomas Spring – how about spring? *(Sings)* "In springtime ..."

Catherine Stand still.

Thomas Or why don't we get married this Christmas?

Catherine I don't think the King would like that.

Thomas He wouldn't mind. We could have a feast – he'd like that! We could invite all our friends.

Catherine Thomas, there's something I have to tell you.

Elizabeth runs in. Edward comes in behind her. He has a blindfold on. They are playing blind man's buff. He bumps into Thomas and makes him drop the presents.

Thomas Look out! Edward!

Edward grabs hold of Thomas.

Edward Who's this? It can't be Daddy – you're too thin. I know! You're Maggie the maid!

Elizabeth Wrong! You're wrong! It's Uncle Thomas.

Edward takes the blindfold off.

Edward Well, Lizzie, see if you can do any better.

5

Elizabeth I don't have to. You didn't catch me. *(She starts to chant)* Can't catch me-ee, can't catch me-ee …

Mary comes in. She is carrying a prayer book.

Mary Do you have to make so much noise? I was trying to pray.

Edward You're always praying.

Catherine Oh come now, Mary, don't be cross. It's Christmas after all. *(To Thomas)* Please ask the King when he would like to see the children.

Thomas But you still haven't told me …

Catherine We'll talk later.

Thomas bows and goes out.

Edward Auntie Catherine, you be Blind Man!

Catherine Later, Edward. Will you help me pick the presents up?

Edward I don't see why I should do that. I'm a prince and I'm going to be King. Princes don't pick things up.

Catherine If you help me pick them up, you can open the first one.

Edward Oh, all right then.

Catherine and Edward pick up the presents.

Mary *(whispering to Elizabeth)* Why should she tell us what to do?

Elizabeth I like Auntie Catherine.

Mary *(crossly)* She's not your aunt.

Elizabeth I think she's going to marry Daddy.

Mary Nonsense!

Elizabeth It's not nonsense. I heard him talking about it.

Mary You're making it up! Who was he talking to?

Elizabeth I'm not telling you.

Mary What did he say?

Elizabeth I'm not telling you.

Mary You didn't hear anything! I don't believe you.

Edward There! Done! I want to open a present. I want to open a present now!

Catherine All right. This one's from Mary.

Edward tears off the paper.

Edward (*sadly*) It's a prayer book. I want a ship. One like Daddy's ship, the *Mary Rose*, with sails and things! (*He starts to cry.*)

Catherine (*gently*) Edward, say "thank you" to Mary.

Edward No! (*To Mary*) When I'm King, I shall order you to give me good presents.

Mary Here we go again!

Edward Well, I shall be King. I'm Daddy's heir.

Elizabeth We know that, Edward, and it's not fair. Mary's older than you. So am I. You shouldn't be the heir. You're the heir, it's not fair. You're the heir, it's not fair. You're the ...

8

Edward Stop it! I'm the heir because you're girls. Girls can't be King.

Elizabeth Girls can be Queens.

Edward Well, Mary isn't going to be Queen, and nor will you. I'm going to be King. Daddy says so. Mary won't be Queen unless something happens to me.

Mary Don't tempt me!

Edward Auntie Catherine! She's bullying me!

Catherine Mary!

Mary I'm sick and tired of it! Edward, Daddy's pet. Cry baby, Edward!

Edward *(to Mary)* At least Daddy loved my Mummy.

Catherine Edward …

Edward (*still talking to Mary*)
Daddy didn't love your
Mummy. He sent her away.

Mary Don't you dare
say that!

Elizabeth Leave Mary alone!

Edward (*to Elizabeth*) And
Daddy had your
Mummy's head chopped
off! (*He acts it out*) Swish! Thump!

Catherine That will do! This is Christmas, the time
of goodwill. Edward, don't tease Mary.

Edward But I …

Catherine Edward, tell Mary you're sorry.

Edward Sorry.

Catherine And Mary's sorry, too – aren't you,
Mary?

Mary glares at Catherine.

Catherine Mary – it is Christmas. A time for love.

Mary nods crossly.

Catherine Good – then we're all friends again. Will
Sommers is coming soon to make us all
laugh.

Mary Oh, not Will Sommers. He's the worst jester in the world!

Elizabeth Auntie Catherine, he's rotten. And he's got bad breath, and he just shouts, "I say, I say, I say ..."

Catherine We'll see, shall we? Now, whose turn is it to open a present?

Edward It's still mine! I want a good present – not a stupid prayer book!

Catherine Well, I have a present for you, Edward. I have some good news. Can you guess what it is?

Edward shakes his head.

Catherine Edward, you're going to be married.

Edward *(horrified)* Married? What ... you mean ... to a girl?

Elizabeth No, to a chicken! What do you think, silly?

Catherine Elizabeth, please! Edward, you are going to be betrothed to a princess.

Edward What does "beetrooted" mean?

Mary Betrothed. It means you've got to marry her.

Edward   But I don't want to get married to a soppy girl! Girls don't do anything interesting. They just dance and do sewing. Wait a moment! Did you say a princess?

Catherine   *(smiling)* That's right.

Edward   Oh well, that's different. I don't mind so much if she's a princess. What's her name?

Catherine   Mary.

Edward   Oh, no! Not another Mary.

Mary   *(crossly)* Mary's a very good name.

Edward   Hmmm. Is she beautiful?

Catherine   So people say. I haven't seen her myself.

Edward   Is she rich?

Catherine   Yes.

Edward   How old is she?

Catherine   I'm not sure. About three …

Edward   *(shocked)* Three years old?

Catherine   Three months old.

Elizabeth and Mary laugh.

Edward   What? I'm not marrying a baby!
Babies dribble and blow bubbles and
keep on being sick all over the place!
I want to marry a beautiful princess,
not change her nappies!

Catherine   You don't have to marry her now,
you silly. You won't get married
until you're King.

Edward   You're not to call me silly. I'm going to
be King!

Edward sulks. Will Sommers, the King's jester, enters.

Will Sommers   I say, I say, I say!

Elizabeth   *(to Catherine)* I told you that's what
he'd say!

Will Sommers Riddle me this! What is brown and sticky?

Elizabeth and Mary *(bored)* A stick.

Will Sommers Oh – you've heard it. I know! Knock knock.

Edward Come in.

Will Sommers No, no. You say "Who's there?"

Edward Why? We know it's you. We can see you.

Will Sommers It's a joke. You have to say "Who's there?"

Elizabeth Who's there?

Will Sommers Mary.

Nobody says anything.

Will Sommers You say "Mary who?"

Catherine Mary who?

Elizabeth and Mary *(bored)* Mary Christmas.

Will Sommers Oh, you've heard that one as well.

Mary We've heard them all. You've been telling the same jokes since I was a little girl.

Thomas enters with more presents.

Thomas What are you doing here, Jester? We don't need you.

Catherine Thomas, that's not very kind.

Thomas Why should I be kind? He made up some stupid joke about my name last week – he said he wanted to "See more" of me. Very funny. Your jokes are as old as you are!

Will Sommers Well, here's a brand new joke for you. When will Catherine Parr not be Catherine Parr?

Elizabeth I don't know.

Will Sommers When she's Queen Catherine!

Thomas *(slowly)* What do you mean, Jester?

Elizabeth *(to Mary)* I told you! I told you! Daddy's going to marry Auntie Catherine!

Thomas *(to Will)* Be gone!

Will Sommers exits.

Thomas *(to Catherine)* Is this true? I must know. Is it true?

Catherine It's true. I was going to tell you later. The King spoke to me yesterday. He asked me to marry him.

Elizabeth Told you! Told you!

Thomas But you're going to marry me! He knows that! I'll not have it. I'll go and tell him.

Catherine And if you do, you'll have your head cut off. There's nothing we can do. I shall have to marry him.

Thomas I see. You want to be Queen. I'll not stand in your way. *(He bows)* My lady.

Thomas exits.

Catherine Thomas! That's not what I meant at all!

Edward Are you going to be our Mummy?

Mary I'm losing count of the mothers I've had.

Catherine Children – it's not what I want. Do you understand? We all have to do what the King says.

Elizabeth Will you be a good mother?

Catherine Yes. I promise.

Elizabeth So that's our Christmas present – a new mother.

Edward I'd rather have a ship.

Mary Edward!

Edward But I suppose a new mother is better than nothing.

Elizabeth and Mary nod.

Catherine Thank you. Now let us go and find the King. Perhaps this year, we can have a real family Christmas.

They exit.

What happened next?

In 1543 King Henry VIII did marry Catherine Parr.
She was his wife and nurse until he died in 1547.

Then Catherine Parr married
Thomas Seymour, but she died
a year later.

Edward became King Edward VI when
his father died. He was nine years old.
He died in 1553 at the age of 15.

After Edward
died, Mary became
Queen. She put
Elizabeth in
prison. Mary
died in 1558.

Then Elizabeth became
Queen Elizabeth I.

READY, STEADY, ACT!

Now that you have read this play it's time to act it out. You will tell your audience the story using words, actions and maybe some costumes and props.

CHOOSING THE PARTS

- Mary is a solemn woman who knows what is right and tries to do it.
- Edward is spoilt. He gets angry or cries when he can't get his own way.
- Catherine is kind, sensible and motherly.
- Elizabeth is cheerful and chatty but stubborn.
- Will Sommers always has a big grin and tries too hard to be funny.
- Thomas is a serious adult who thinks he is very important.

Who in your cast would be best at these roles? Try reading sections of the play and taking turns at different parts. Make name stickers for the characters to wear.

> Did you know...?
> King Henry VIII had over 78,000 people executed while he was king.

SETTING THE SCENE

The action takes place in an English palace during the reign of Henry VIII. How will you show your audience that the play takes place in the past?

You could play some music from Tudor times. Perhaps you could have live music played on recorders.

The play opens in a candlelit room. Could you create this effect without candles? Can you make it dark? Can you find some torches and wrap them in paper? If adults agree, try night lights in jam jars.

Get into groups of three or four and freeze-frame a scene from the play. Take turns at showing your scene. Can the rest of the group guess who you are? Think about how you stand and the look on your face.

WHAT YOU WILL NEED

Costumes

There are all sorts of ways to show that you are in Tudor times.

- You could make cloaks using lengths of cloth.
- You can make paper crowns.
- Boys can tuck their trousers into long socks.
- Waistcoats and hats will add to the look.
- Girls can wear long, full skirts and jewellery.
- You could make false beards, or use facepaints.

The pictures will give you some ideas.

Props

You will need a stack of presents, so perhaps each cast member can bring a wrapped, empty box.

Will Sommers has a jester's stick. You could make one yourself based on the pictures, or use a baby's rattle.

If you use a blindfold for the game, take care that the actors can still see.

Sound effects

Think about how to use your music in the performance. Find places in the script where it would be good to play some music. You could have different music for different characters.

SPEAKING AND MOVING

In this play you will need to show excitement, disappointment, tension, boredom and humour. Some of the characters are adults. They will speak and move in different ways from the children.

Speaking

Speak clearly and slowly. Make sure the audience knows what your character feels. Try saying, 'I'm looking for my present', as if you are excited, upset, worried, angry and tired. Now practise saying your lines from the play in a way that clearly shows how you are feeling.

Moving

Freeze-frame the illustration on page 6. Try to make your faces like the picture as well as your bodies. When someone calls 'Action!', move into another frozen picture. Move as if you are wearing real costumes of the time, slowly and stiffly.

What next?

Once you have performed this play you might want to:

- find some new jokes for the jester
- use your music to develop a Tudor dance.